THE ROYAL HORTICULTURAL SOCIETY
Diary 2000

Johann Gesner (1709-1770)

Commentary by Brent Elliott

FRANCES LINCOLN

Frances Lincoln Limited
4 Torriano Mews
Torriano Avenue
London NW5 2RZ

The Royal Horticultural Society Diary 2000
Copyright © Frances Lincoln 1999

British Library cataloguing-in-publication data
A catalogue record for this book is available from the British Library

ISBN 0-7112-1410-7

Printed in Hong Kong

First Frances Lincoln edition 1999

RHS FLOWER SHOWS 2000

All shows feature a wide range of floral exhibits staged by the nursery trade, with associated competitions
reflecting seasonal changes, and horticultural sundries. With the exception of the shows at Malvern, Chelsea,
Strathclyde, Birmingham, Hampton Court, Tatton Park and Wisley, all RHS Flower Shows will be held in one
or both of the Society's Horticultural Halls in Greycoat Street and Vincent Square, Westminster, London SW1.
In 2000 it is likely that *all* Westminster Shows will be held in the New Hall, Greycoat Street as the Old Hall
will be closed for refurbishment

The dates given are correct at the time of going to press, but before travelling to a Show we strongly advise
you to check with the Diary Dates section of the RHS Journal *The Garden*, or telephone the 24-hour Flower
Show Information Line for the latest details. Tel: 0171 649 1885.

FRONT COVER

The illustrations depict Hexandria, or plants with six stamens. *Narcissus, Galanthus, Leucojum, Pancratiu, Crinum*
and *Amaryllis* (usually regarded as *Hippeastrum*), are now considered as members of Liliaceae, or, by some
botanists, of a smaller family, Amaryllidaceae. *Pontederia* belongs in a different family, Pontederiaceae. On the
back cover, *Ananas*, the pineapple, is now included in Bromeliaceae.

TITLE PAGE

A detail of *Eryngium*, the sea hollies, which Linnaeus included in his family Pentandria, or plants with five
stamens. In 1789 Antoine-Laurent de Jussieu transferred *Eryngium* into a new family, Umbelliferae. The native
English eryngo (*Eryngium campestre*) had a long history of use as a medicinal plant and for making 'kissing
comfits' to sweeten the breath; foreign species began to be imported as garden plants in the early 17th century.

OPPOSITE INTRODUCTION

This plate shows Decandria, or plants with ten stamens. Left to right, from the top: *Dianthus, Saponaria,
Gypsophila, Bufonia, Moehringia, Silene* (which now includes *Cucubalus*), *Stellaria, Arenaria, Cherleria, Alsine,
Corrigiola, Holosteum, Queria, Sagina, Spergula, Lychnis, Cerastium,* and *Agrostemma*. Almost all can be recognised
today as belonging to a single natural category: Caryophyllaceae, the carnation family. The exceptions are *Drymis*
(Winteraceae), *Pharnaceum* and *Mollugo* (Molluginaceae), *Montia* (Portulacaceae), and *Geranium* (Geraniaceae).

Calendar 2000

January
M	T	W	T	F	S	S
					1	2
3	4	5	6	7	8	9
10	11	12	13	14	15	16
17	18	19	20	21	22	23
24	25	26	27	28	29	30
31						

February
M	T	W	T	F	S	S
	1	2	3	4	5	6
7	8	9	10	11	12	13
14	15	16	17	18	19	20
21	22	23	24	25	26	27
28	29					

March
M	T	W	T	F	S	S
		1	2	3	4	5
6	7	8	9	10	11	12
13	14	15	16	17	18	19
20	21	22	23	24	25	26
27	28	29	30	31		

April
M	T	W	T	F	S	S
					1	2
3	4	5	6	7	8	9
10	11	12	13	14	15	16
17	18	19	20	21	22	23
24	25	26	27	28	29	30

May
M	T	W	T	F	S	S
1	2	3	4	5	6	7
8	9	10	11	12	13	14
15	16	17	18	19	20	21
22	23	24	25	26	27	28
29	30	31				

June
M	T	W	T	F	S	S
			1	2	3	4
5	6	7	8	9	10	11
12	13	14	15	16	17	18
19	20	21	22	23	24	25
26	27	28	29	30		

July
M	T	W	T	F	S	S
					1	2
3	4	5	6	7	8	9
10	11	12	13	14	15	16
17	18	19	20	21	22	23
24	25	26	27	28	29	30
31						

August
M	T	W	T	F	S	S
	1	2	3	4	5	6
7	8	9	10	11	12	13
14	15	16	17	18	19	20
21	22	23	24	25	26	27
28	29	30	31			

September
M	T	W	T	F	S	S
				1	2	3
4	5	6	7	8	9	10
11	12	13	14	15	16	17
18	19	20	21	22	23	24
25	26	27	28	29	30	

October
M	T	W	T	F	S	S
						1
2	3	4	5	6	7	8
9	10	11	12	13	14	15
16	17	18	19	20	21	22
23	24	25	26	27	28	29
30	31					

November
M	T	W	T	F	S	S
		1	2	3	4	5
6	7	8	9	10	11	12
13	14	15	16	17	18	19
20	21	22	23	24	25	26
27	28	29	30			

December
M	T	W	T	F	S	S
				1	2	3
4	5	6	7	8	9	10
11	12	13	14	15	16	17
18	19	20	21	22	23	24
25	26	27	28	29	30	31

Calendar 2001

January
M	T	W	T	F	S	S
1	2	3	4	5	6	7
8	9	10	11	12	13	14
15	16	17	18	19	20	21
22	23	24	25	26	27	28
29	30	31				

February
M	T	W	T	F	S	S
			1	2	3	4
5	6	7	8	9	10	11
12	13	14	15	16	17	18
19	20	21	22	23	24	25
26	27	28				

March
M	T	W	T	F	S	S
			1	2	3	4
5	6	7	8	9	10	11
12	13	14	15	16	17	18
19	20	21	22	23	24	25
26	27	28	29	30	31	

April
M	T	W	T	F	S	S
						1
2	3	4	5	6	7	8
9	10	11	12	13	14	15
16	17	18	19	20	21	22
23	24	25	26	27	28	29
30						

May
M	T	W	T	F	S	S
	1	2	3	4	5	6
7	8	9	10	11	12	13
14	15	16	17	18	19	20
21	22	23	24	25	26	27
28	29	30	31			

June
M	T	W	T	F	S	S
				1	2	3
4	5	6	7	8	9	10
11	12	13	14	15	16	17
18	19	20	21	22	23	24
25	26	27	28	29	30	

July
M	T	W	T	F	S	S
2	3	4	5	6	7	8
9	10	11	12	13	14	15
16	17	18	19	20	21	22
23	24	25	26	27	28	29
30	31					

August
M	T	W	T	F	S	S
		1	2	3	4	5
6	7	8	9	10	11	12
13	14	15	16	17	18	19
20	21	22	23	24	25	26
27	28	29	30	31		

September
M	T	W	T	F	S	S
					1	2
3	4	5	6	7	8	9
10	11	12	13	14	15	16
17	18	19	20	21	22	23
24	25	26	27	28	29	30

October
M	T	W	T	F	S	S
1	2	3	4	5	6	7
8	9	10	11	12	13	14
15	16	17	18	19	20	21
22	23	24	25	26	27	28
29	30	31				

November
M	T	W	T	F	S	S
			1	2	3	4
5	6	7	8	9	10	11
12	13	14	15	16	17	18
19	20	21	22	23	24	25
26	27	28	29	30		

December
M	T	W	T	F	S	S
					1	2
3	4	5	6	7	8	9
10	11	12	13	14	15	16
17	18	19	20	21	22	23
24	25	26	27	28	29	30
31						

Johann Gesner (1709-1770)

The Swiss botanist Johann Gesner was born in Zürich. He was still in his teens when he started climbing in the Alps looking for plants. In 1726 he went to Leiden in the Netherlands, to study at the Botanic Garden under Hermann Boerhaave. He then moved to the Jardin des Plantes in Paris, where he worked under Bernard de Jussieu. On returning to Switzerland, he studied mathematics under Johann Bernoulli. One of his fellow students was Albrecht von Haller, a year his senior: he and Haller became best friends and the two went plant-hunting together in the mountains around Basle.

Gesner became a teacher of mathematics and medicine at Basle, and was appointed Professor in 1738. By now he and Haller were working together on a flora of Switzerland. But Gesner's health began to fail and he had to give up his plant-collecting expeditions; then Haller was appointed to a professorship in Göttingen, so their collaboration ended. Haller continued with the work, publishing it in 1742 under the title *Enumeratio methodica stirpium Helvetiae indigenarum,* and acknowledging Gesner's contribution in his preface. Haller went on to compile the major Swiss flora of the century; Gesner turned his attention to wider botanical matters.

In the early 1740s Gesner encountered the writing of Linnaeus, and − after a few years in which letters went astray − the two men became enthusiastic correspondents. Linnaeus described Gesner in one letter as 'a man whom I esteem above all other botanists'. By now, Gesner had started work on a history of plants − a systematic classification of the plant world − a task that he could carry out without the fieldwork he had had to give up; and Linnaeus, then working on his own *Species plantarum*, was eager to exchange ideas and plant specimens. Gesner's plan was for a richly illustrated work setting out comparative details of the different plant families on composite plates for ease of comparison.

Linnaeus' system of classification was based on sexual reproduction: the primary differences between plants lay in their sexual organs. His major plant groups were distinguished by the number of their stamens: Monandria (one stamen), Diandria (two stamens), and so on, up to Dodecandria (12-19 stamens) and Polyandria (twenty or more); then further groups for plants with stamens of unequal length, stamens united in bundles, stamens and pistils on separate flowers or on different plants, and lastly Cryptogamia, plants that reproduced without seeds.

In 1763 Gesner sent Linnaeus copies of the first two printed plates of his intended publication − and Linnaeus responded that he was 'thunderstruck' by their quality. Unfortunately, Gesner died before the work was completed, and Linnaeus did not live to see the book's publication. It was 1795 before Christian Salomon Schinz finally began the process of seeing Gesner's manuscript through the press.

The printing of Gesner's book continued until 1826, with the last plates unaccompanied by text. By then, Linnaeus' system of classification was coming under attack from a new generation of botanists, and Gesner's work never acquired the reputation or influence it might have done had it appeared during his lifetime.

In 1789 Antoine-Laurent de Jussieu published his *Genera plantarum*, proposing a 'natural classification' in which all characteristics of a plant would be taken into account; he was succeeded by Robert Brown, Alphonse de Candolle, John Lindley and others, all of whom added new concepts to classification. Jussieu grouped plants into a series of natural orders, which his successors categorized as 'families' (this is how they are referred to, for convenience, in the following captions). Some of these families bore names consisting of the name of a characteristic genus followed by the suffix -aceae (for example Papaveraceae, Liliaceae); during the 19th century, this became the standard model for new family names. Other Jussieu family names were not based on the name of a particular genus but simply related to the family as a whole: Gramineae, for example, is the Latin name for grains. Other examples include Palmae (palms) and Umbelliferae (umbel-carrying plants). Some of these names survive, although there have been frequent attempts to replace them with names in the modern standard form.

Names and groupings of families, genera and species have been changeable and controversial throughout the history of plant classification. The captions that follow give some idea of how they have changed over the past two centuries.

Brent Elliott
The Royal Horticultural Society

Tab. 30

C.C. Geißler Del. et Sculp. Add. Polygonum 1.9 Ortegia 8 Scleranthus 16 Glinus 31 Velezia 62 Minuartia 73

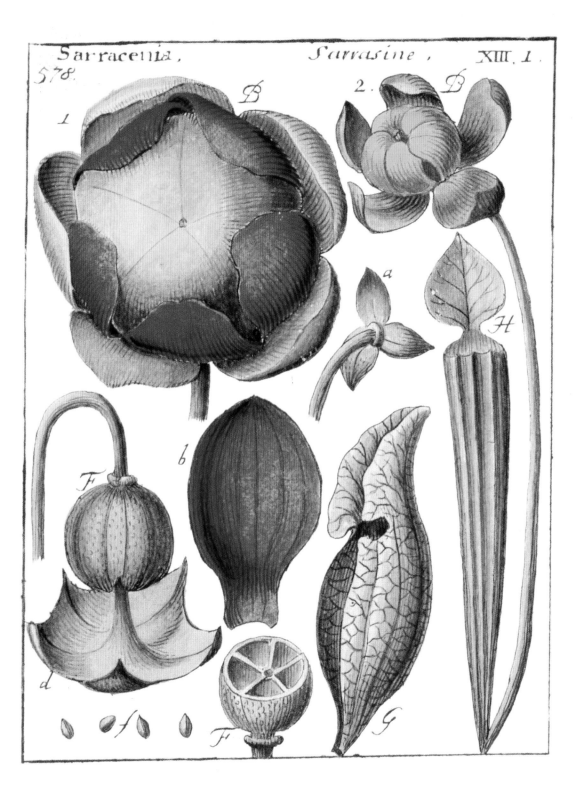

December 1999/January 2000 Week 52

27 Monday

Holiday, UK, Republic of Ireland,
Canada, Australia and New Zealand

28 Tuesday

Holiday, UK, Republic of Ireland,
Canada, Australia and New Zealand

29 Wednesday

Last Quarter

30 Thursday

31 Friday

Holiday (observed), USA
Holiday, UK (Millennium Bank Holiday)

1 Saturday

New Year's Day

2 Sunday

Sarracenia, a genus which Linnaeus included in
Icosandria, or plants with about twenty stamens;
he named the genus after the French physician
Michel Sarrazin, who had sent the plant to Europe
from Canada at the beginning of the 18th century.
Jussieu relegated *Sarracenia* to a category of plants
of whose classification he was unsure. In 1829 the
French botanist B. C. J. Dumortier resolved the
problem by creating a separate family called
Sarraceniaceae.

3   Monday

Holiday (observed), UK, Republic of Ireland,
Canada, Australia and New Zealand

4   Tuesday

Holiday, Scotland and New Zealand

5   Wednesday

6   Thursday

New Moon
Epiphany

7   Friday

8   Saturday

9   Sunday

This plate depicts Icosandria, or plants with about twenty stamens. *Cactus*, in the top row, was moved by Jussieu into a separate family, Cacti (now Cactaceae), and the single genus he recognized has since been divided into 97 different genera. Of the remainder, *Sarracenia* is now in Sarraceniaceae, *Nymphaea* in Nymphaeaceae, *Aizoon* and *Tetragonia* in Aizoaceae, *Portulaca* in Portulacaceae, while *Mesembryanthemum* is sometimes included in Aizoaceae and sometimes in Mesembryanthemaceae.

533. Heliocarpus, Sonenfrucht, XI. 2.

529 Triumfetta, Bermudische Klette, XI. 1.

10 Monday

14 Friday

<small>First Quarter</small>

11 Tuesday

15 Saturday

12 Wednesday

16 Sunday

13 Thursday

Heliocarpus, which Linnaeus included in Polyandria, or plants with more than twenty stamens, is now included in the lime family Tiliaceae. This genus of ten species is from tropical America, where some of the species are used locally as sources of fibre.

17 Monday

Holiday, USA (Martin Luther King's birthday)

18 Tuesday

RHS Flower Show

19 Wednesday

RHS Flower Show

20 Thursday

21 Friday

Full Moon

22 Saturday

23 Sunday

This plate depicts Polyandria, or plants with more than twenty stamens. The following now form part of Jussieu's family Tiliaceae, the lime family: *Muntingia, Tilia, Heliocarpus, Triumfetta, Bartramia* (now included in *Triumfetta*), *Corchorus* and *Grewia*. Of the remainder, *Clusia* is now in Guttiferae (or sometimes Clusiaceae), *Bixa* in Bixaceae, *Sloanea* in Elaeocarpaceae, *Dillenia* in Dilleniaceae, *Theobroma* (chocolate) in Sterculiaceae and *Kiggelaria* in Flacourtiaceae.

Tab. 37.

Classis XIII. POLYANDRIA VIELFÆDICHTE. A. Monogynia.

I. CVLMINEÆ. BALCKENPFLANTZEN.

Muntingia Americ. 575 Mesplen-Baum.

Clusia, Balsam Baum. 577 XXIII. 3

581 Bixa, Vrucu, Orleans,

Sloanea, Nackenbaum, Apeiba. 582.

Tilia, Lindenbaum. 587.

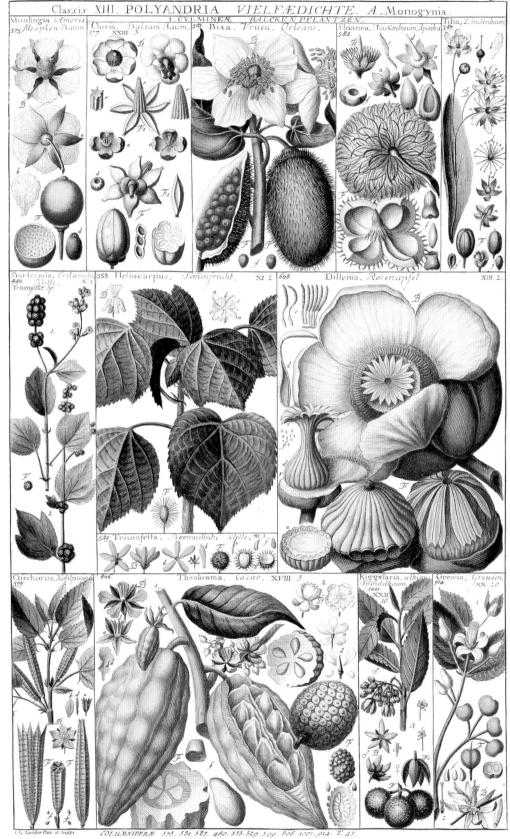

Bartramia, Ceilandis. 480 Klette. X. 1. Triumfettæ Sp.

533 Heliocarpus, Sonenfrucht. XI. 2.

608 Dillenia, Rosenapfel XIII. 2.

529 Triumfetta, Bermudische Klette. XI. 1

Corchorus, Kohlpappel 599.

806 Theobroma. Cacao. XVIII. 5

Kiggelaria, althiop. Spindelbaum. 1001 XXII. 10

Grewia, Grewen. 914. XX. 20

509. Banisteria Schlingender Ahorn.
X/3.

B

F

24   Monday

25   Tuesday

26   Wednesday

Holiday, Australia (Australia Day)

27   Thursday

28   Friday

Last Quarter

29   Saturday

30   Sunday

Linnaeus included the genus *Banisteria* in Heptandria, or plants with seven stamens. In the early 19th century, the German botanist Karl Sigismund Kunth absorbed *Banisteria* into the genus *Heteropterys*, in the family Malpighiaceae; most botanists ignored this categorization until the 20th century, but it is now accepted. In 1910 the Canadian botanist Charles Budd Robinson moved nine of the species into a new genus, *Banisteriopsis*.

---

31   Monday

---

1   Tuesday

---

2   Wednesday

---

3   Thursday

---

4   Friday

---

5   Saturday

New Moon
Chinese New Year

---

6   Sunday

Holiday, New Zealand (Waitangi Day)

Heptandria and Octandria: plants with seven and eight stamens respectively. The Heptandria are now: *Aesculus* (Hippocastanacaeae), *Acer* (Aceraceae), *Begonia* (Begoniaceae), *Staphylea* (Staphyleaceae); *Paullinia, Cardiospermum, Sapindus* (Sapindaceae); *Malpighia, Banisteria, Triopterys* (Malpighiaceae). Octandria: *Osbeckia, Rhexia, Memecylon* (Melastomataceae); *Oenothera, Gaura, Epilobium, Ludwigia, Jussiaea* [now included in *Ludwigia*] (Onagraceae); *Mimusops* (Sapotaceae), *Lawsonia* (Lythraceae), *Daphne, Dirca, Gnidia, Stellera, Passerina, Lachnaea* (Thymelaceae) and *Paris* (Trilliaceae).

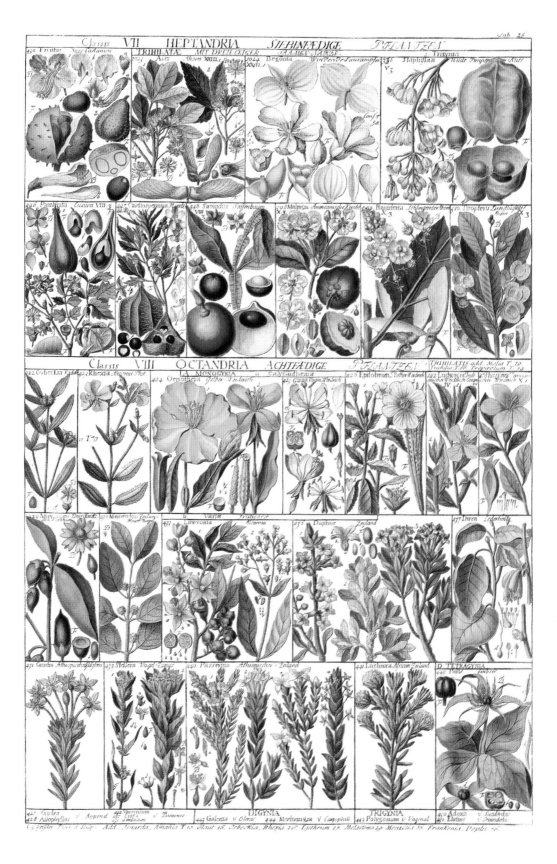

Tab. 46

February 2000

7 Monday

8 Tuesday

9 Wednesday

10 Thursday

11 Friday

Rachel Flame

12 Saturday

First Quarter
Lincoln's birthday

13 Sunday

In 1789 Jussieu included the palm *Areca* in his family Palmae. To bring it into line with the majority of family names, which attach the suffix -aceae to the name of the characteristic genus, the 19th-century German botanist Carl Heinrich Schultz proposed replacing Palmae with Arecaceae. This proposal is still controversial, but has been widely accepted in America (and by the RHS *Plant Finder*).

---

14 Monday

St Valentine's Day

---

15 Tuesday

RHS Flower Show

---

16 Wednesday

RHS Flower Show

---

17 Thursday

---

18 Friday

---

19 Saturday

Full Moon

---

20 Sunday

This plate depicts Hexandria, or plants with six stamens. Almost all of them - *Areca, Phoenix, Cocos, Elate* (now included in *Phoenix*), *Chamaerops, Borassus, Corypha* and *Caryota* - can be recognized as belonging to a single natural group, which Jussieu called Palmae. The exception is *Cycas*, a Gymnosperm, more closely related to conifers than to palms and which Jussieu placed in Filices. In 1807 the Dutch botanist Persoon named the family Cycadaceae.

Tab. 22

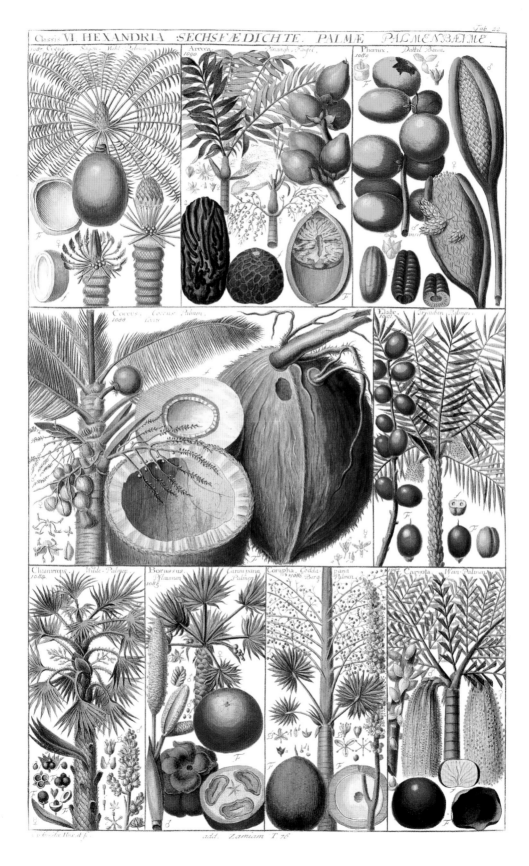

55. **Gladiolus. Feder-Lilie.**

February 2000

21 Monday

Holiday, USA (Presidents' Day)

22 Tuesday

23 Wednesday

24 Thursday

25 Friday

26 Saturday

27 Sunday

Last Quarter

Linnaeus included the genus *Gladiolus* in Triandria, or plants with three stamens; Jussieu in 1789 transferred it into his family Irides, now called Iridaceae. Of the nearly 200 European and African species, most of the gladioli grown as ornamental plants are of South African origin; their ancestors were first imported through Holland in the late 17th century, and were being hybridized by the early 19th century.

28   Monday

29   Tuesday

1   Wednesday

St David's Day

2   Thursday

3   Friday

4   Saturday

5   Sunday

This plate depicts Triandria, or plants with three stamens. Most of these fall into Iridaceae: *Crocus, Ixia, Gladiolus, Antholyza, Sisyrinchium* and *Iris. Commelina* was transferred into a new family, Commelinaceae, by Robert Brown in 1810. *Colchicum* (which now includes *Bulbocodium*) and *Aphyllanthes* have long been included in Liliaceae, but many botanists place them in separate families, Colchicaceae and Aphyllanthaceae. *Xyris* and *Eriocaulon* are now located in the families Xyridaceae and Eriocaulaceae.

Tab. 4

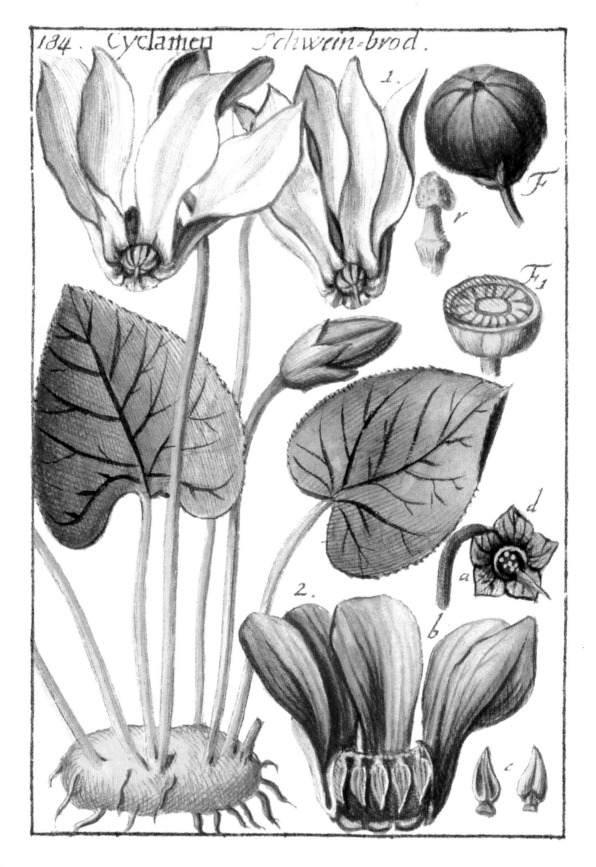

184. Cyclamen Schwein-brod.

6   Monday

Danielle 15

New Moon

7   Tuesday

Shrove Tuesday

8   Wednesday

Ash Wednesday

9   Thursday

10   Friday

11   Saturday

12   Sunday

Linnaeus included *Cyclamen* in Pentandria, or plants with five stamens. It now belongs in Primulaceae, a family established in 1799 by the French botanist Ventenat. Cyclamens have been grown as ornamental plants since the 16th century, beginning with European and moving on to west Asian species; but the most popular species, *Cyclamen persicum*, despite its name, comes not from Persia but from the area of the Balkans and the Aegean.

13 Monday

First Quarter
Commonwealth Day

14 Tuesday

RHS Flower Show

15 Wednesday

RHS Flower Show

16 Thursday

17 Friday

St Patrick's Day
Holiday, Northern Ireland and Republic of Ireland

18 Saturday

RHS London Orchid Show

19 Sunday

RHS London Orchid Show

The plants in this plate of Pentandria, or plants with five stamens, fall mostly into two families. *Swertia, Gentiana, Chironia* and *Exacum* are now in Gentianaceae, as was *Menyanthes* before it was moved to Menyanthaceae. *Androsace* (including the former genus *Aretia*), *Primula, Cortusa, Soldanella, Dodecatheon, Cyclamen, Hottonia, Lysimachia, Anagallis* and *Samolus* are now Primulaceae. The remainder are: *Diapensia* (Diapensiaceae), *Sarothra* (Clusiaceae), *Theophrasta* (Theophrastaceae), *Patagonula* (Boraginaceae), *Ophiorrhiza* and *Randia* (Rubiaceae) and *Plumbago* (Plumbaginaceae).

Tab. 12.

Classis V. PENTANDRIA FÜNF-FÆDICHTE A Monogynia b Monopetalæ capsula intra florem

March 2000

---

20 Monday

Full Moon
Vernal Equinox

---

21 Tuesday

---

22 Wednesday

---

23 Thursday

---

24 Friday

---

25 Saturday

---

26 Sunday

British Summer Time begins

This plate shows *Narcissus*, a genus which Linnaeus included in Hexandria, or plants with six stamens, and which Jussieu moved into his family Narcissi. In 1810 Robert Brown transferred it into Amaryllideae, which Lindley renamed Amaryllidaceae. Meanwhile, in 1806, the Swiss botanist Alphonse de Candolle expanded Jussieu's family Liliaceae to include *Narcissus*, and his classification is still generally accepted today. However some botanists divide Liliaceae and return *Narcissus* to Amaryllidaceae.

March/April 2000

27 Monday

28 Tuesday

Last Quarter

29 Wednesday

30 Thursday

31 Friday

1 Saturday

2 Sunday

Mothering Sunday

This plate depicts Hexandria, or plants with six stamens. *Ananas* (the pineapple) and *Tillandsia* are now included in Bromeliaceae, *Renealmia* in Zingiberaceae, *Burmannia* in Burmanniaceae, *Tradescantia* in Commelinaceae and *Pontederia* in Pontederiaceae. The rest of the plants have long been included in Liliaceae. Many botanists today break Liliaceae up into smaller units, so that *Galanthus*, *Leucojum*, *Narcissus*, *Pancratium*, *Crinum* and *Amaryllis* (the last-named usually regarded as *Hippeastrum*) all fall into the family Amaryllidaceae.

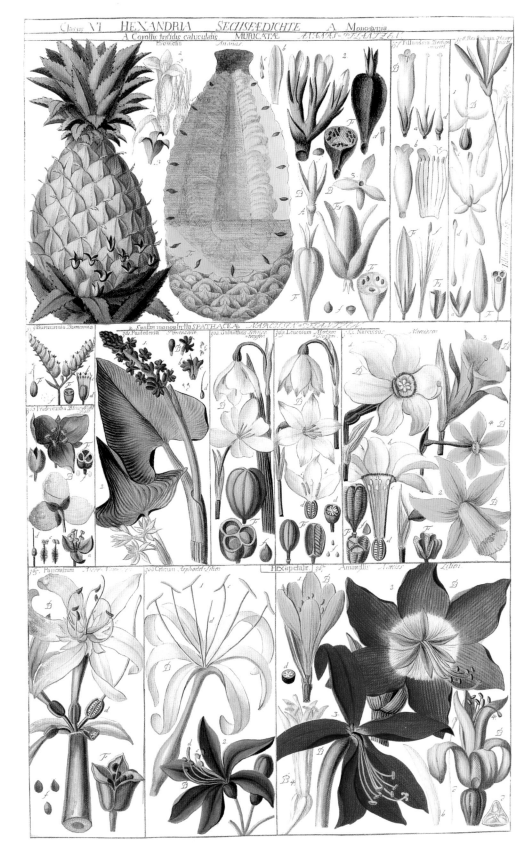

195. Azalea yeiss=Rare. V.2.l.

April 2000

3 Monday

7 Friday

4 Tuesday

8 Saturday

New Moon

5 Wednesday

9 Sunday

5 Wednesday

Linnaeus' genus *Azalea* is still familiar to all as a horticultural category, if not properly a botanical one. In 1834 the Scottish plant collector and botanist George Don argued that *Azalea* and *Rhodododendron* were not distinct, and that the former should be included in the latter. John Claudius Loudon replied that the proposal, 'however technically correct' was 'injudicious in a practical point of view', but Don's proposal gradually won acceptance.

Islamic New Year (subject to sighting of the moon)

April 2000

10 Monday

11 Tuesday

First Quarter
RHS Flower Show

12 Wednesday

RHS Flower Show

13 Thursday

14 Friday

15 Saturday

16 Sunday

Palm Sunday

This plate depicts Decandria, or plants with ten stamens. Several of these genera now form part of Ericaceae: *Kalmia, Ledum, Rhododendron* (which has absorbed *Azalea), Andromeda, Vaccinium, Erica, Blaeria, Epigaea, Gaultheria, Arbutus, Pyrola* and *Monotropa. Clethra* is now in Clethraceae, *Trientalis* in Primulaceae, *Myrsine* in Myrsinaceae, *Empetrum* in Empetraceae, *Melastoma* and *Memecylon* in Melastomataceae, *Santalum* in Santalaceae, *Ruta* in Rutaceae and *Melia* in Meliaceae. *Diospyros,* which has absorbed *Royena,* is in Ebenacea and *Schinus* in Anacardiaceae.

Tab. 29

173. Aspenigo Gross-Kleb-Khaut.   175. Echium Blaue=Ochsen-Zunge.

C. G. Geissler. Pinx. et Sculps.   Add. Varronia, Ehretia T. 65.

April 2000

17 Monday

18 Tuesday

Full Moon

19 Wednesday

20 Thursday

Maundy Thursday
Passover (Pesach) First Day

21 Friday

Good Friday
Holiday, UK, Republic of Ireland,
Canada, Australia and New Zealand
Birthday of Queen Elizabeth II

22 Saturday

23 Sunday

Easter Sunday
St George's Day

Two plants which Linnaeus included in
Pentandria, or plants with five stamens. In 1789
Jussieu grouped them into his new family of
Borragineae (now Boraginaceae). *Asperugo
procumbens*, the only species in that genus, is the
madwort, so called because it yielded a pigment
resembling madder (*Rubia tinctoria*). There are 60
species of *Echium* scattered around Eurasia and
Africa, some increasingly grown as ornamental
plants.

24 Monday

Easter Monday
Holiday, UK (exc. Scotland), Republic of Ireland,
Canada, Australia and New Zealand

25 Tuesday

Holiday, Australia and New Zealand (Anzac Day)
RHS Flower Show

26 Wednesday

Last Quarter
Passover (Pesach) Seventh Day
RHS Flower Show

27 Thursday

Passover (Pesach) Eighth Day

28 Friday

29 Saturday

30 Sunday

This illustration depicts Pentandria, or plants with five stamens. Top row, left to right: *Heliotropium*, *Myosotis* (forget-me-not), *Lithospermum*, *Anchusa*, and *Pulmonaria*. Second row: *Cynoglossum*, *Symphytum*, *Cerinthe* and *Borago* (borage). Bottom row: *Asperugo*, *Echium*, *Lycopsis*, *Tournefortia* and *Hydrophyllum*. This last genus was chosen by Robert Brown in 1817 to be the typical genus of a new family called Hydrophyllaceae; all the others fall into Jussieu's family Borragineae (now called Boraginaceae).

Tab. II.

164 Heliotropium Sonnen-...   165 Myosotis Blauer Augentrost   166 Lithospermum Steinhirse   167 Anchusa Ochsen-Zunge   168 Pulmonaria Lungen-Kraut

168 Cynoglossum Hunds-Zunge   170 Symphytum Wallwurtz   171 Cerinthe Wachs-Kraut   172 Borrago Borretsch

173 Asperugo Grass-Kleb-Kraut   175 Echium Blaue Ochsen-Zunge   174 Lycopsis Wolfs-Zunge   176 Tournefortia Tournefortie   177 Hydrophyllum Wasserblatt

Add. Varronia, Ehretia T. 68. Cordia T. 17. Patagonula T. 12. Nolana T. 13.

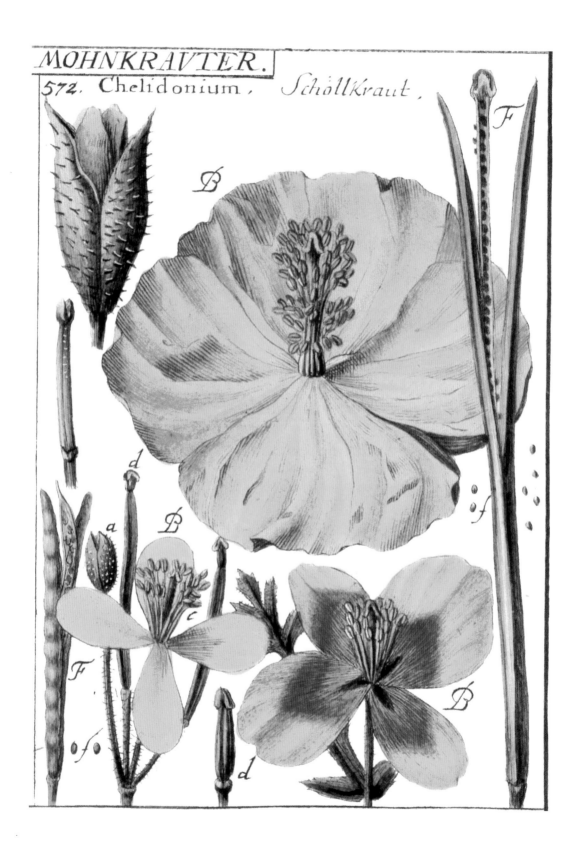

572. Chelidonium, Schöllkraut,

May 2000

---

1   Monday

May Day Holiday, UK (exc. Scotland) and Republic of Ireland
Spring Holiday, Scotland

---

2   Tuesday

---

3   Wednesday

---

4   Thursday

New Moon

---

5   Friday

Malvern Spring Gardening Show

---

6   Saturday

Malvern Spring Gardening Show

---

7   Sunday

Malvern Spring Gardening Show

Linnaeus included the genus *Chelidonium*, in Polyandria, or plants with more than twenty stamens; Jussieu included it in Papaveraceae, the poppy family. There is only one species, *Chelidonium majus*, distributed throughout temperate Eurasia, which was introduced into England in the Middle Ages as a medicinal plant.

8   Monday

9   Tuesday

10 Wednesday

First Quarter

11 Thursday

12 Friday

13 Saturday

14 Sunday

Mother's Day, Canada and USA

This plate depicts Polyandria, or plants with more than twenty stamens. *Actaea* is included in Jussieu's family Ranunculaceae, *Podophyllum* in Berberides (now Berberidaceae) and *Bocconia*, *Sanguinaria*, *Chelidonium*, *Papaver* and *Argemone* in Papaveraceae. *Cistus* became the basis of Cisti (now Cistaceae); *Hypericum* and *Ascyrum*, now included in *Hypericum*, moved into his Guttiferae (and is now sometimes included in Clusiaceae); while *Telephium*, which Jussieu included in Portulacaceae, has wandered through Caryophyllaceae and Molluginaceae, depending on the botanist one consults.

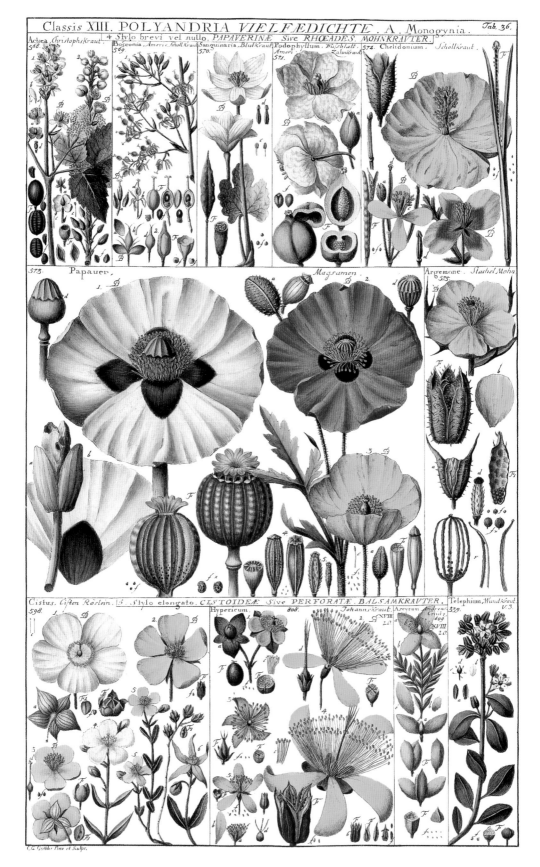

Tab. 36.

Classis XIII. POLYANDRIA *VIELFÆDICHTE*. A. Monogynia.

4 Stylo brevi vel nullo. *PAPAVERINÆ* Sive *RHOEADES. MOHNKRAUTER*.

Actæa. *Christophskraut*. 568.

Bocconia. *Americ. Scholkraut*. 569.

Sanguinaria. *Blutkraut*. 570.

Podophyllum. *Füsblatt*. *Ameri*. 571.

Chelidonium. *Schollkraut*. 572.

573. Papauer.

Magsamen.

Argemone. *Stachel Mohn*. 575.

Cistus. *Cisten Röslein*. 5. Stylo elongato. *CISTOIDEÆ* Sive *PERFORATÆ. BALSAMKRAUTER*. 598.

Hypericum. 808.

Johannskraut. *Ascyrum. Andreas Creutz*. 409.

Telephium. *Wundkraut*. V.3. 339.

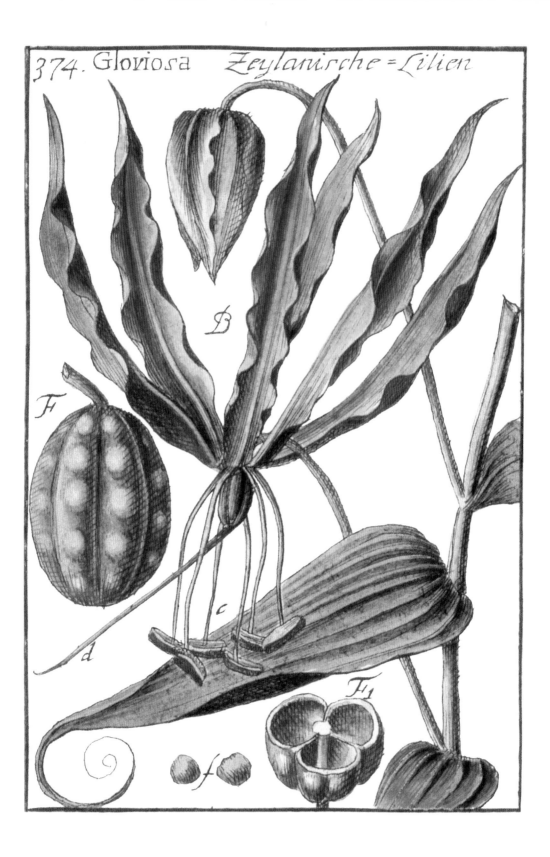

15 Monday

19 Friday

16 Tuesday

20 Saturday

17 Wednesday

21 Sunday

18 Thursday

Full Moon

Gloriosa, the flame lily, is a genus which Linnaeus included in Hexandria, or plants with six stamens, and which in 1789 became part of Jussieu's new family Liliaceae. There seems to be no certainty about the number of species, or how many things that have been treated as different species are in fact merely varieties. *Gloriosa superba* was introduced into England by the Earl of Portland at the end of the 17th century.

22 Monday

Holiday, Canada (Victoria Day)

23 Tuesday

Chelsea Flower Show

24 Wednesday

Chelsea Flower Show

25 Thursday

Chelsea Flower Show

26 Friday

Last Quarter
Chelsea Flower Show

27 Saturday

Chelsea Flower Show

28 Sunday

This plate depicts Hexandria, or plants with six stamens, all of which were included by Jussieu in Lilia, now called Liliaceae. Many botanists today break Liliaceae up into smaller units, so that *Haemanthus* falls into Amaryllidaceae, *Allium* into Alliaceae, *Gloriosa* and *Uvularia* into Colchicaceae, *Ornithogalum* and *Scilla* into Hyacinthaceae, *Asphodelus* into Asphodelaceae, and *Anthericum* into Anthericaceae; while *Fritillaria*, *Erythronium*, *Tulipa* and *Lilium* remain in the true Liliaceae.

Tab. 24.

Classis VI. HEXANDRIA. SECHSFÆDICHTE. A Hexapdalæ. LILIACEÆ. LILIEN-PFLANTZEN.

394. Hæmanthus Africanische Tulpan. 370. Allium Cepa, Porrum, Knoblauch, Zwiebel, Lauch.

371. Lilium Lilien. 372. Fritillaria Corona-Imperialis, Fritillarie, Kayser-Krone.

374. Gloriosa Zeylanische-Lilien. 373. Uvularia Zapfen-Kraut. 375. Erythronium Hunds-Zahn. 376. Tulipa Tulipan.

377. Ornithogalum Milch-Stengel. 378. Scilla Meer-Zwiebel. 379. Asphodelus Gold-wurtz. 380. Anthericum Lederpinen-Kraut.

530.Peganum *Geiss Raute.* 532.Lythrum *Weidkraut.*

May/June 2000

29 Monday

Spring Holiday, UK (exc. Scotland)
May Day Holiday, Scotland
Holiday, USA (Memorial Day)

30 Tuesday

31 Wednesday

1 Thursday

Ascension Day

2 Friday

New Moon
Scotland's National Gardening Show, Strathclyde

3 Saturday

Scotland's National Gardening Show, Strathclyde

4 Sunday

Scotland's National Gardening Show, Strathclyde

This plate shows two members of Linnaeus' family Dodecandria, or plants with twelve stamens. On the left is *Peganum* (Zygophyllaceae), a genus used for producing hallucinogenic alkaloids. On the right is *Lythrum* (loosestrife and related herbs), which in 1805 was made the typical genus of a new family called Lythraceae by the French botanist Jaume Saint-Hilaire.

June 2000

5   Monday

Holiday, Republic of Ireland
Holiday, New Zealand (Queen's birthday)

6   Tuesday

7   Wednesday

8   Thursday

9   Friday

First Quarter
Jewish Feast of Weeks (Shavuot)

10 Saturday

The Queen's official birthday (subject to confirmation)

11 Sunday

Whit Sunday (Pentecost)

The upper half of this plate depicts Enneandria, or plants with nine stamens. Top row: *Laurus* (now in Lauraceae) and *Spondias,* grouped by John Lindley into Anacardiaceae in 1830. Second row: *Rheum* (rhubarb), *Rumex* (docks), *Polygonum* and *Atraphaxis,* all grouped by Jussieu into Polygoneae (now Polygonaceae). The bottom row depicts Dodecandria, or plants with twelve stamens. *Gethyllis* is now in Liliaceae; *Rhizophora* – a genus which includes the mangroves – in Rhizophoraceae; *Peganum* (Zygophyllaceae); *Lythrum* (Lythraceae) and *Glinus* (Molluginaceae).

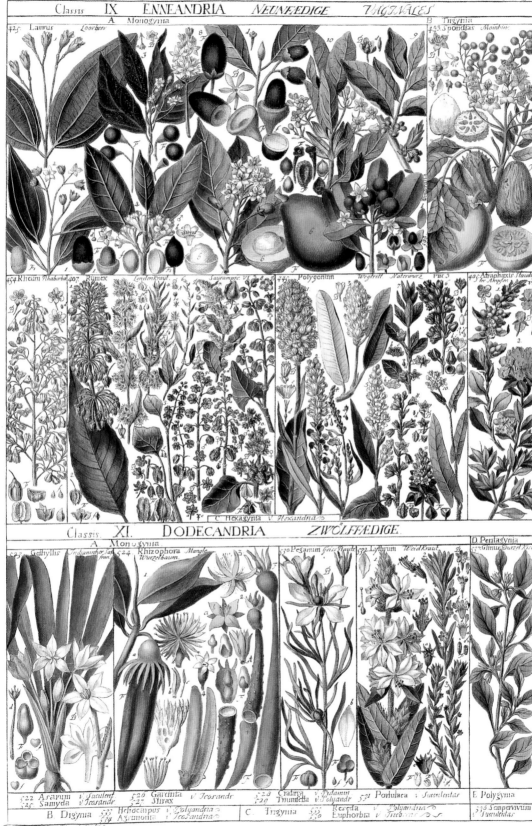

Tab. 27.

Classis IX ENNEANDRIA NEUNEEDIGE VAGINALES

A Monogynia

425 Laurus Loorbeer

B Trigynia
453 Spondias Mombin

454 Rheum Rhabarber 407 Rumex Lenckenkraut Saurampre VI Polygonum Wegtritt Naterwurz rue 3 405 Atraphaxis Staudiger Ampfer Abyssen VI 2

C Hexagynia V Hexandria

Classis XI. DODECANDRIA ZWÖLFFEEDIGE.

A Monogynia

523 Gethyllis Indianischer Safran fruit 524 Rhizophora Wurzelbaum Mangle 530 Peganum Gaiss Reute 532 Lythrum Weidkraut

D Pentagynia
533 Glinus Surzed Rice

522 Asarum v Juculent 526 Garcinia v Icosandr 528 Crataeva v Putamin 531 Portulaca v Succulentas
525 Samyda v Icosandr 527 Styrax 529 Trumistia v Polyandr

B Digynia 533 Heliocarpus v Polyandria C Trigynia 529 Reseda v Polyandria
524 Agrimonia v Icosandria 530 Euphorbia v Tricticas

E Polygynia
535 Sempervivum
v Succulentas

C.A.Spisler. Pinx et Sculps.

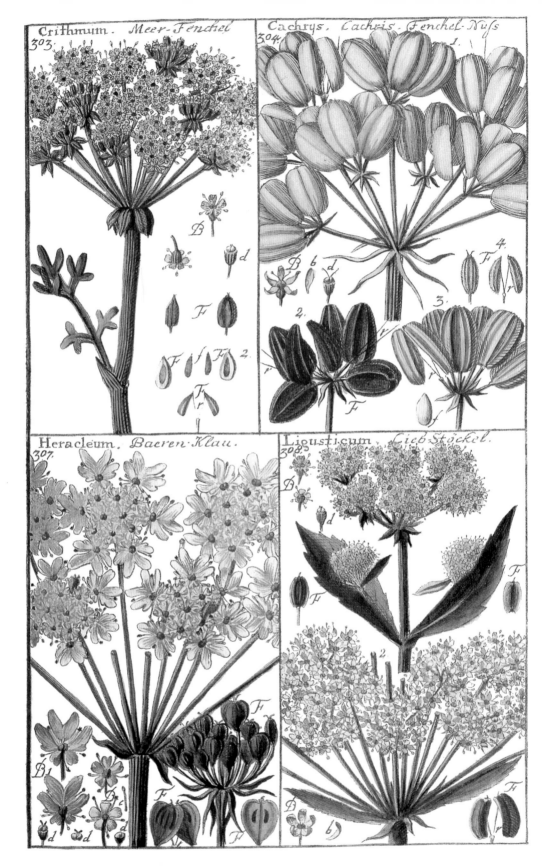

Crithmum. Meer-Fenchel

303.

Cachrys. Cachris. Fenchel-Nuss

304. 1.

Heracleum. Baeren-Klau.

307.

Liousticum. Lieb-Stöckel.

308.

12 Monday

Holiday, Australia (Queen's birthday)

13 Tuesday

14 Wednesday

BBC Gardener's World Live, Birmingham
(to be confirmed)

15 Thursday

BBC Gardener's World Live, Birmingham
(to be confirmed)

16 Friday

Full Moon
BBC Gardener's World Live, Birmingham
(to be confirmed)

17 Saturday

BBC Gardener's World Live, Birmingham
(to be confirmed)

18 Sunday

Trinity Sunday
Father's Day, UK, Canada and USA
BBC Gardener's World Live, Birmingham
(to be confirmed)

Linnaeus included the four genera shown here in
Pentandria, or plants with five stamens; Jussieu
moved them into Umbelliferae. *Crithmum
maritimum*, the only species in its genus, is the sea
samphire, much used in pickling; *Cachrys* has eight
species, mostly Mediterranean; there are over 60
species of *Heracleum*, the hogweeds, across the
northern hemisphere; some of the 40-odd species
of *Ligusticum* are used as medicinal plants by
American Indians.

June 2000

19 ~~Monday~~

Amy + Jamie Tilles

20 Tuesday

RHS Flower Show

21 Wednesday

Summer Solstice
RHS Flower Show

22 Thursday

Corpus Christi

23 Friday

24 Saturday

25 Sunday

Last Quarter

The plants in this plate of Pentandria, or plants with five stamens, can still be recognized today as belonging to a single natural group, which Jussieu in 1789 named Umbelliferae (now sometimes called Apiaceae): plants in which the flowers are carried in an inflorescence called an umbel. Top row: *Conium, Selinum, Athamanta, Peucedanum*; second row: *Crithmum, Cachrys, Ferula, Laserpitium*; third row: *Heracleum, Ligusticum, Angelica, Sium*; bottom row: *Sison, Bubon* (now included in *Athamanta*), *Cuminum* and *Oenanthe*.

Tab. 14

Classis V. PENTANDRIA. *FVNFFÆDICHTE.* B. Digynia. *GYMNODISPERMÆ UMBELLIFERÆ. FEYCHELKRÆTER.*

299. Conium.   Wuetrich.   Selinum. *Wild-Peterlein Oelsenisch.*   Athamanta.   *Bær-Wurtz.*   302. Peucedanum. *Haar-Strang.*

b. Involucro partiali et universali

300.   301. Athamanta Cervaria

303. Crithmum. *Meer-Fenchel.*   504. Cachrys. *Cachrys Fenchel-Nuss.*   505. Ferula. *Galban-Staude.*   506. Laserpitium. *Hirsch-Wurtz.*

307. Heracleum. *Bæren-Klau.*   508. Ligusticum. *Lieb-Stöckel.*   509. Angelica. *Angelica.*   310. Sium. *Eppich.*

311. Sison. *Feldamomsl. Sichel-Kraut.*   312. Bubon. *Macedonischer Peterlein.*   313. Cuminum. *Kümmel.*   Oenanthe. *Schierling-Raute.*

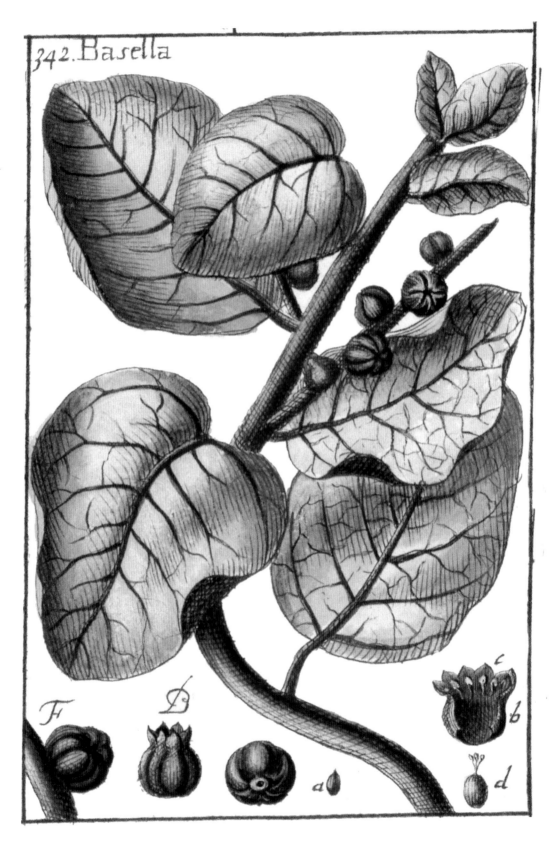

342.Basella

26 Monday

First Wisley Flower Show (to be confirmed)

27 Tuesday

First Wisley Flower Show (to be confirmed)

28 Wednesday

29 Thursday

30 Friday

1 Saturday

New Moon
Holiday, Canada (Canada Day)

2 Sunday

Linnaeus included the genus *Basella* in Pentandria, or plants with five stamens. In 1840 the French botanist Moquin-Tandon made it the characteristic genus of a new family, Basellaceae (although some botanists give the credit for this family to the eccentric American botanist C. S. Rafinesque). There are five species of *Basella*, all tropical herbs, with *B. rubra* sometimes known as Indian spinach.

---

3   Monday

Holiday (observed), Canada

---

4   Tuesday

Holiday, USA (Independence Day)
Hampton Court Palace Flower Show

---

5   Wednesday

Hampton Court Palace Flower Show

---

6   Thursday

Hampton Court Palace Flower Show

---

7   Friday

Hampton Court Palace Flower Show

---

8   Saturday

First Quarter
Hampton Court Palace Flower Show

---

9   Sunday

Hampton Court Palace Flower Show

Of the plants included in this plate of Pentandria, or plants with five stamens, the only ones that belong in the same families today are *Viburnum* and *Sambucus* (Caprifoliaceae) and *Zanthoxylum* and *Barreria* [now *Diosma*] (Rutaceae). The others are: *Rhus* (Anacardiaceae), *Cassine* (Celastraceae), *Rondeletia* (Rubiaceae), *Bellonia* (Gesneriaceae), *Coriaria* (Coriariaceae), *Berberis* (Berberidaceae), *Callicarpa* (Verbenaceae), *Tamarix* (Tamaricaceae), *Basella* (Basellaceae), *Parnassia* (Parnassiaceae), *Aralia* (Araliaceae), *Linum* (Linaceae) and *Suriana* (Surianaceae).

Tab. 21.

C Trigynia. *DUMOSÆ*

331 Rhus Gerber-baum 332 Viburnum Meel-baum 333 Cassine Thee aus Paraguai

334 Sambucus Holder-staude 335 Zanthoxylum Fragula-staude 336 Rondeletia V.I. 337 Bellonia V.I.

1002 Coriaria XXII. 1. 399 Berberis Erbseln-staude V.I. 327 Callicarpa IV 1. 337 Tamarix Tamarisken-staude 342 Basella

330 Staphylæa 1. Trihelatas 328 Turnera 1. Malvaceas 339 Telephium 1. Succulentas
340 Corrigiola 341 Pharnaceum 342 Alsine 1. Caryophylleas.

D Tetragynia. E Pentagynia.

345 Parnassia Parnassis-blum 347 Bartera 346 Aralia Beeij- Angelica 349 Limum Flaus 350 Suriana X.1

DUMOSIS add. T. 15. 231. 240. 350 Aldrovanda } 1. Inundatas.
Achras T. 86. Prinos T. 76. IlexL. 351 Drosera } 1. Succulentas. 354 Sibbaldia 1. Icosandria
Schinus T. 24. Fagara T. 84. 352 Crassula HEDERACEÆ. 335. 346. Hedera - 17iti Cissus L. 59. Panax T. 18.

F Polygynia.
355 Myosurus 1. Polyandria

Lonicera   Geissblatt

July 2000

10 Monday

11 Tuesday

12 Wednesday

Holiday, Northern Ireland (Battle of the Boyne)

13 Thursday

14 Friday

15 Saturday

St Swithin's Day

16 Sunday

Full Moon

Linnaeus included the genus *Lonicera* in Pentandria, or plants with five stamens; it now belongs in Jussieu's family Caprifoliaceae. The traditional Latin name of the honeysuckle had been Periclymenum, but Linnaeus renamed it *Lonicera* after Adam Lonitzer, whose *Kreütterbuch* was one of the most frequently reprinted of Renaissance herbals. Ironically it was also one of the worst, being a compilation of extracts from various earlier herbals edited together by Lonitzer, the publisher's son-in-law.

July 2000

17 Monday

18 Tuesday

19 Wednesday

20 Thursday

The RHS Flower Show, Tatton Park

21 Friday

The RHS Flower Show, Tatton Park

22 Saturday

The RHS Flower Show, Tatton Park

23 Sunday

The RHS Flower Show, Tatton Park

This plate depicts Pentandria, or plants with five stamens. *Phlox* and *Polemonium* now belong to Polemoniaceae; *Convulvulus* and *Ipomoea* to Convulvulaceae; *Campanula, Phyteuma, Jasione, Trachelium, Roella* and *Lobelia* to Campanulaceae; *Genipa, Cinchona, Mussaenda, Ixora* and *Coffea* to Rubiaceae; *Diervilla, Lonicera* and *Triosteum* to Caprifoliaceae; and *Loranthus* to Loranthaceae.

Phlox,   Lichnidee.
197.

II Capsula intra florem. CAMPANACEÆ, GLOGGENPFLANZEN.
Convolvulus,   Winde.   Evolvulus v. T. 73.
198.

Ipomoea, Federwinde.
199.

Polemonium, Griech.Baldrian
200.

III. Monopetalæ, germine infra florem. A CAMPANACEÆ.
Campanula,   Gloggen-   blume.

Phyteuma, Rapunzel
203.

Iasione, Schaaf Scabiosa.
895. XIX. 5.

Roella, Afric: Stachel-Glogge.
202.

Trachelium,   Kehl Kraut.
206.

B. Variæ et CYMOSÆ, GIPFEL-PFLANZEN.
Genipa, Junipaba, Baum.
229.

Lobelia, Cardinals-Blume.
897.   XIX. 5.

Viola v. T. 649.

Cinchona, Fieber-Rinde.
206.

Diervilla, Diervilla
Lonicera v. Specit10.

Lonicera   Geissblatt.
210.

211. Triosteum.

Loranthus, Riemen-Blume.   400.
VI. 1.

Musænda, Belilla-Staude.
214.

Ixora, Malabar-Iasmin.
122.   IV. 1.

Coffea, Coffe-Baum.
209.

Rondeletia, Bellonia, v. Dumosas.

July 2000

24 Monday

Last Quarter

25 Tuesday

26 Wednesday

27 Thursday

28 Friday

29 Saturday

30 Sunday

Linnaeus included the genus *Holcus* in Triandria, or plants with three stamens; Jussieu moved it into his family Gramineae. The 19th-century Italian botanist Teodoro Caruel proposed changing this name to Poaceae (using *Poa* as the characteristic genus); but while botanists in several countries now accept this name and treat the bamboos as a separate family, Bambusaceae, Gramineae is still the family name in general use.

31 Monday

New Moon

1 Tuesday

2 Wednesday

3 Thursday

4 Friday

5 Saturday

6 Sunday

This plate depicts Triandria, or plants with three stamens. All of these plants now belong in Gramineae, the grass or grain family, which Jussieu established in 1789. Top row: *Avena* (oats), *Lagurus*, *Arundo*, *Aristida*, *Apluda*. Middle row: *Lolium*, *Elymus*, *Secale* (rye), *Hordeum* (barley), *Triticum* (wheat). Bottom row: *Andropogon*, *Holcus*, *Ischaemum*, *Cenchrus* and *Aegilops*.

Tab 7

Classis III. TRIANDRIA DREYEÆDICHTE. GRAMINA. GRÆSER. B. Digynia. 2. calyce plerumque multifloro.

Ch. Gottscher. Pinx. et Sculp.

Amygdalus. *Mandel-Baum, Pfersich-Baum.*

August 2000

7   Monday

First Quarter
Summer Holiday, Scotland
Holiday, Republic of Ireland

8   Tuesday

9   Wednesday

10   Thursday

11   Friday

12   Saturday

13   Sunday

Linnaeus included the genus *Amygdalus* in Icosandria, or plants with about twenty stamens; in 1789 Jussieu moved it into his new family Rosaceae. In 1812 the physician Jonathan Stokes suggested that *Amygdalus* should be absorbed into *Prunus*, which includes the peach, the apricot and the plum, and after a period of resistance, the almond *Amygdalus communis* became, first, *Prunus amygdalus*, and eventually *Prunus dulcis.*

14 Monday

15 Tuesday

Full Moon
RHS Flower Show

16 Wednesday

RHS Flower Show

17 Thursday

18 Friday

19 Saturday

20 Sunday

All the plants in this plate of Icosandria, or plants with about twenty stamens, can be recognized as belonging to a single natural category, which Jussieu established as the family Rosaceae. Top row: *Prunus*, which now includes *Amygdalus* (the almond). Second row: *Spiraea* and *Rosa*. Third row: *Rubus*, *Fragaria*, *Potentilla* and *Tormentilla* (now included in *Potentilla*). Bottom row: *Comarum* (now in *Potentilla*), *Sibbaldia*, *Geum*, *Dryas* and *Agrimonia*.

Tab. 34.

Classis XII. ICOSANDRIA, ZWANTZIGFÆDICHTE. DRVPACEÆ. COMOSÆ. SENTICOSÆ.
PFLAVMENAR TIGE. BVSCHE. GESTRAVCHE.

MONOGYNIÆ. D. DRVPACEÆ. PFLAVMENARTIGE.

545. Amygdalus. Mandel-Baum. Pfersich-Baum.   546. Prunus. Pflaumen-Baum. Schlehen. Zwetschge. Kirschenbaum.

b. Comosæ. E. PENTA- et POLYGYNIÆ. b. Senticosæ.

554. 1. Spiraca. 2. Spier-Staude. Gessebart. Vlmaria.   556. Rosa. Rose.

Rubus. 557. Brombeer. Zänkeer. Staude.   Fragaria. 558. Erd-beer.   Potentilla. 559. Ginzerich. Fünf-finger-kraut.   Tormentilla. 560. Tormentill.

Comarum. 563. Roth Fünger Kraut.   Sibbaldia. 554. Sibbaldie.   Geum. 561. Caryophyllata. Benedicten-Wurtz.   Dryas. 542. Berg-Benedicten.   Agrimonia. 544. Odermenig.

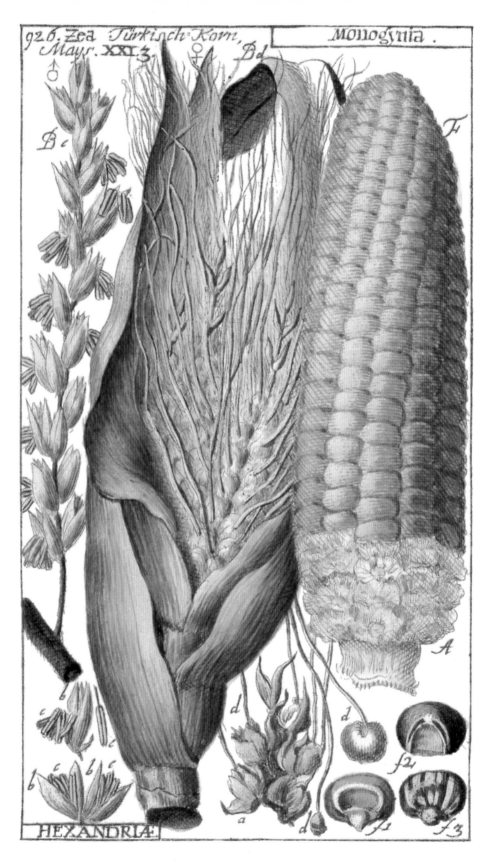

926. Zea Türkisch-Korn, Mays. XXI.3

Monogynia.

HEXANDRIA

21 Monday

25 Friday

22 Tuesday

26 Saturday

Last Quarter
Second Wisley Flower Show (to be confirmed)

23 Wednesday

27 Sunday

Second Wisley Flower Show (to be confirmed)

24 Thursday

Zea, a genus which Linnaeus included in Triandria, or plants with three stamens, and which Jussieu in 1789 moved into Gramineae, the grass or grain family (and which is now frequently included in Poaceae). There are four species of *Zea*, all from Central America, the most important of which is *Zea mays*, now cultivated worldwide as maize or sweetcorn.

28 Monday

Summer Holiday, UK (exc. Scotland)

29 Tuesday

New Moon

30 Wednesday

31 Thursday

1 Friday

Angie

2 Saturday

3 Sunday

This plate depicts Triandria, or plants with three stamens. *Schoenus, Scirpus, Cyperus, Eriophorum* and *Carex* belong to Jussieu's family Cyperaceae. *Lygeum, Nardus, Zea, Coix, Oryza* and *Zizania* are all Gramineae. Jussieu classified *Calamus* into Palmae and *Juncus* into Junci (now Juncaceae); Dumortier later made *Flagellaria* the characteristic genus of Flagellariaceae, while Achille Richard moved *Scheuchzeria* and *Triglochin* into his new family Juncaginaceae.

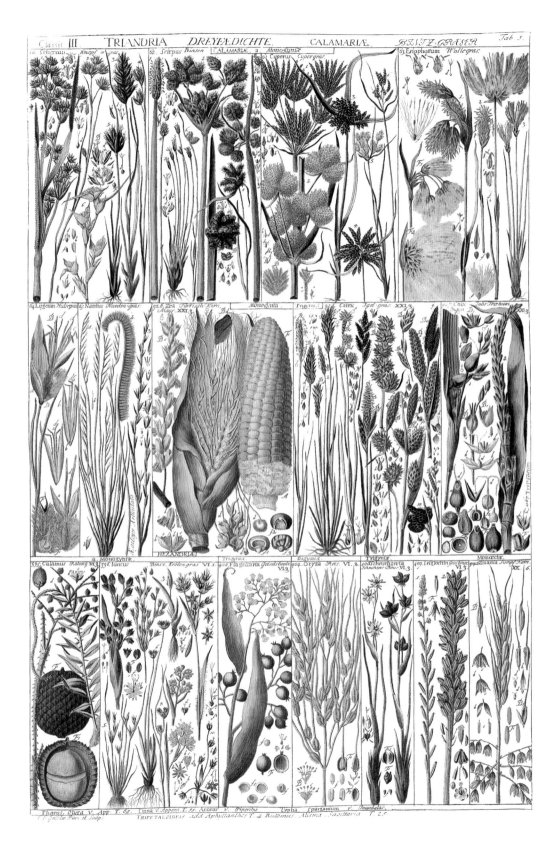

Capsicum. Indianischer Pfeffer.

225.

226.

1.

B

b

d

a

d

1.

F

f

F

2.

f f

F

B

2.

F

f

September 2000

4 Monday	8 Friday
Holiday, Canada (Labour Day) and USA (Labor Day)	
5 Tuesday	9 Saturday
First Quarter	
6 Wednesday	10 Sunday
7 Thursday	

Two genera which Linnaeus included in Pentandria, or plants with five stamens. Jussieu moved *Capsicum,* the caper plant, into his Solaneae (now Solanaceae) and *Strychnos,* from which the drug strychnine is obtained, into Apocineae (now Apocynaceae). In the 1820s Robert Brown moved *Strychnos* into his new family Loganiaceae. The Swiss botanist Alphonse de Candolle proposed a new family, Strychnaceae, in which both genera belonged, and this proposal has been revived by some modern botanists.

11 Monday

15 Friday

12 Tuesday

16 Saturday

RHS Great Autumn Show

13 Wednesday

17 Sunday

Full Moon
RHS Great Autumn Show

14 Thursday

This plate depicts Pentandria, or plants with five stamens. Most of those shown here – *Datura, Hyoscyamus, Nicotiana, Mandragora, Atropa, Physalis, Solanum* and *Capsicum* – were included by Jussieu in his family Solaneae, now called Solanaceae. *Mirabilis*, the 'Marvel of Peru', falls into Nyctaginaceae; *Verbascum* (into which *Celsia* has been absorbed) into Scrophulariaceae and *Strychnos* into Loganiaceae.

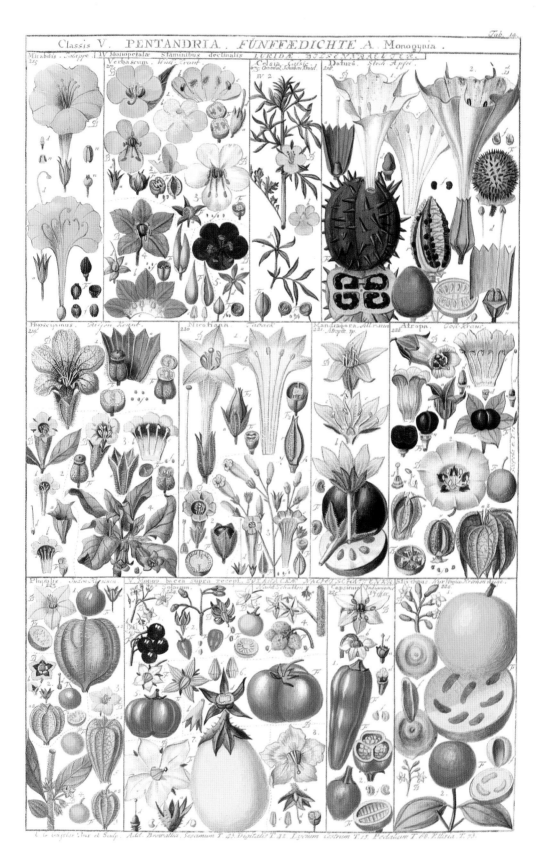

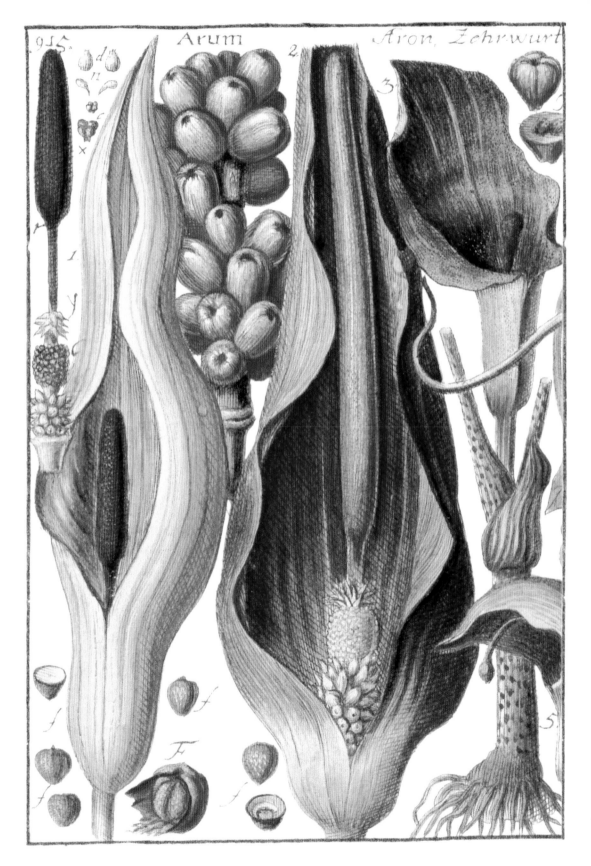

September 2000

18 Monday

19 Tuesday

20 Wednesday

21 Thursday

Last Quarter

22 Friday

Autumnal Equinox

23 Saturday

Malvern Autumn Show

24 Sunday

Malvern Autumn Show

Arum, a genus which Linnaeus included in Diandria, or plants with two stamens. He thought of it as a flower with a single petal; it was only later that it was recognized as a spadix (a spiky inflorescence consisting of many tiny flowers) surrounded by a bract or spathe. In 1789 Jussieu moved *Arum* and a few other spadix-bearing plants into his family Aroideae, now called Araceae.

September/October 2000 Week 39

25 Monday

26 Tuesday

27 Wednesday

New Moon

28 Thursday

29 Friday

Michaelmas Day

30 Saturday

Jewish New Year (Rosh Hashanah)

1 Sunday

This plate of Diandria, or plants with two stamens, clearly illustrates the confusion caused by using a single criterion, such as stamen number, to classify plants. *Piper*, *Saururus* and *Phytolacca* are dicots, now in three separate families, while all the others are monocots, mostly from the family established by Jussieu in 1789 as Aroideae (now called Araceae). The exception is *Zostera*, which Dumortier in 1829 made the basis of a new family, Zosteraceae.

Tab. 3

Classis II. DIANDRIA ZWEYFÄSSICHE. C. Triandria. PIPERITÆ PFEFFERKRÄUTER

42. Piper Pfeffer-baum. Saururus Unnuschuaro Pfeffer 414. VII 3.

424. Phytolacca Laco Amaranth X 10. 392. Acorus Kalmus. VI 1. 394. Orontium Virgin Zehrwurtz. VI 1. 913. Arum Aron Zehrwurtz XX 20.

919. Zostera Meerbinse. XX 20. 918. Pothos Aron Webel. 917. Calla Wasser Aron. XX 20. 916. Dracontium Schlangen-Aron. XX 20.

A. MONOGYNIÆ. 2 Corollis irregularibus. a. Angiosperma. 25.Veronica. 26.Justicia. 27.Gratiola. 28. Pinguicula. 29. Utricularia.
b. Gymnosperma. 30. Verbena. 31.Lycopus. 32. Amethystea. 33. Ziziphora. 34. Monarda. 35. Rosmarinus.
36. Salvia. 37. Dianthera. 38. Collinsonia. c. Dynamias ringentes. 39. Morina. d. Aggregatas.
B. DIGYNIÆ. 40. Anthoxanthum. c. Gramina. 41. Butonia. d. Caryophilleas.
PIPERITIS add. 1233. Ambrosinia T. 70.

C.G. Oeder. Pinx. et Sculps.

348

2   Monday

6   Friday

3   Tuesday

7   Saturday

Nathan

RHS Flower Show

4   Wednesday

8   Sunday

RHS Flower Show

5   Thursday

First Quarter

Statice, a genus which Linnaeus included in Tetrandria, or plants with four stamens, and which Jussieu moved into his new family Plumbagines (now Plumbaginaceae). *Statice* was later divided between two genera, with the sea-lavenders being assigned to *Limonium*, a genus devised by the Chelsea Physic Garden's famous gardener Philip Miller, and the sea-pinks to the German botanist Willdenow's genus *Armeria*. The term *Statice* is nonetheless still used by many people for the sea-lavenders.

9 Monday

Jewish Day of Atonement (Yom Kippur)
Holiday, Canada (Thanksgiving Day)
Holiday, USA (Columbus Day)

10 Tuesday

11 Wednesday

Little Davids

12 Thursday

13 Friday

Full Moon

14 Saturday

Jewish Festival of Tabernacles (Succoth) First Day

15 Sunday

This plate depicts Tetrandria, or plants with four stamens; the genera shown here are now scattered among fourteen different families. Top row: *Leucadendron, Protea* (both Proteaceae) and *Cephalanthus* (Rubiaceae). Second row: *Globularia* (Globulariaceae), *Dipsacus, Scabios* and *Knautia* (all Dipsacaceae). Third row: *Morina* (Morinaceae), *Lantana* (Verbenaceae), *Morinda* (Rubiaceae), *Brunia* (Bruniaceae) and *Conocarpus* (Combretaceae). Bottom row: *Valeriana* (Valerianaceae), *Statice* (Plumbaginaceae), *Hebenstretia* (Scrophulariaceae), *Boerhavia* (Nyctaginaceae) and *Circaea* (Onagraceae).

Tab.6

Classis. IV. TETRANDRIA. VIERFÆDICHTE. I. Monoqunia. A. Plantæ DIPSACEÆ. CARDENKRÆUTER.

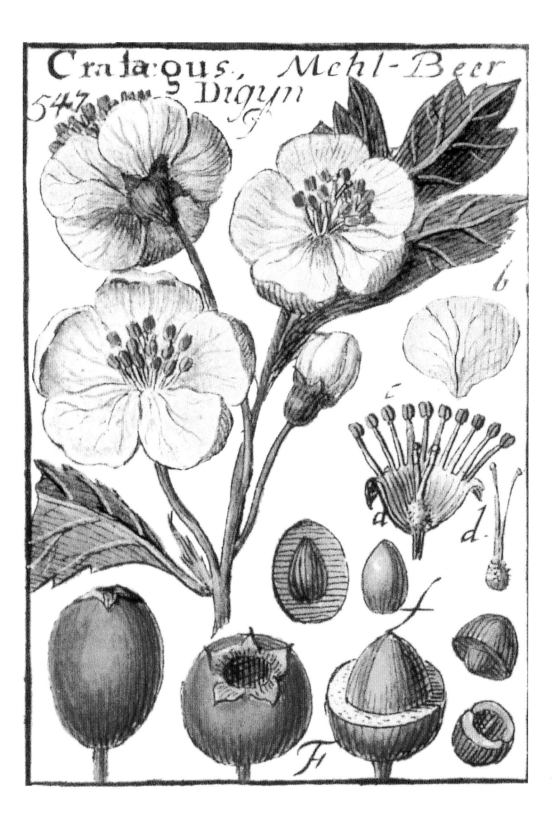

Crataegus, Mehl-Beer
547 Digyn

16 Monday

20 Friday

Last Quarter

17 Tuesday

21 Saturday

Jewish Festival of Tabernacles (Succoth) Eighth Day

18 Wednesday

22 Sunday

19 Thursday

Crataegus, a genus which Linnaeus included in Icosandria, or plants with about twenty stamens, and which Jussieu in 1789 moved into his new family Rosaceae. Although only two of the roughly 200 species are native to Britain, hawthorns have been one of the most widely used of hedging plants, and historic thorn trees have been the occasion for a rich growth of myth and legend.

23 Monday

Holiday, New Zealand (Labour Day)

24 Tuesday

United Nations Day

25 Wednesday

26 Thursday

27 Friday

New Moon

28 Saturday

29 Sunday

British Summer Time ends

This plate depicts Icosandria, or plants with about twenty stamens. *Pyrus* (pear), *Crataegus* (hawthorn), *Sorbus* (rowan) and *Mespilus* (medlar) were moved by Jussieu into his family Rosaceae, and *Eugenia, Psidium* and *Myrtus* into Myrti (now Myrtaceae). *Caryophyllus* now forms part of the genus *Dianthus* (Caryophyllaceae). *Philadelphus* is in Hydrangeaceae, *Punica* (the pomegranate) in Punicaceae, *Ribes* in Grossulariaceae, *Garcinia* in Guttiferae (or Clusiaceae), *Styrax* in Styracaceae, *Citrus* in Rutaceae, and *Samyda* in Flacourtiaceae.

Tab. 23.

Classis XII. ICOSANDRIA ZWANTZIGFÆDICHTE. A. Monoginia.

Philadelphus zimt. Eugenia, Eugenier. Jambo   A. ARBISTILE. Psidium, Guajave. Mirtus, Mirtera. Caryophyllus, NelckenBaum.
546. Roslein. 545.   541.   545.   594.

Punica, Granat apfel Baluster.   550   B. POMACEÆ. OBSTBAUME. Pentagyn.   Pyrus, Birn-Apfel-Quitten-Baum.
544.

Cratægus, Mehl-Beer   Sorbus Sperver-Baum.   549   Mespilus, Mespel-Baum.   Ribes, Johannes-Traüble.
543. Indyn   548. Trigyn.   Pentagyn.   247.

Garcinia, Mangostans.   Citrus, Citronen-Pomeranzen   C. HESPERIDEÆ. ORANGERIEGEWECHSE.   Samyda, Guidonien.
526.   607. Baum.   Diä'nes.   542.

Styrax.   Storax.
527.

C.G. Geisler Pinx et Sculps.   P. C. MACEIS Odci Chrysobalanus T 33.

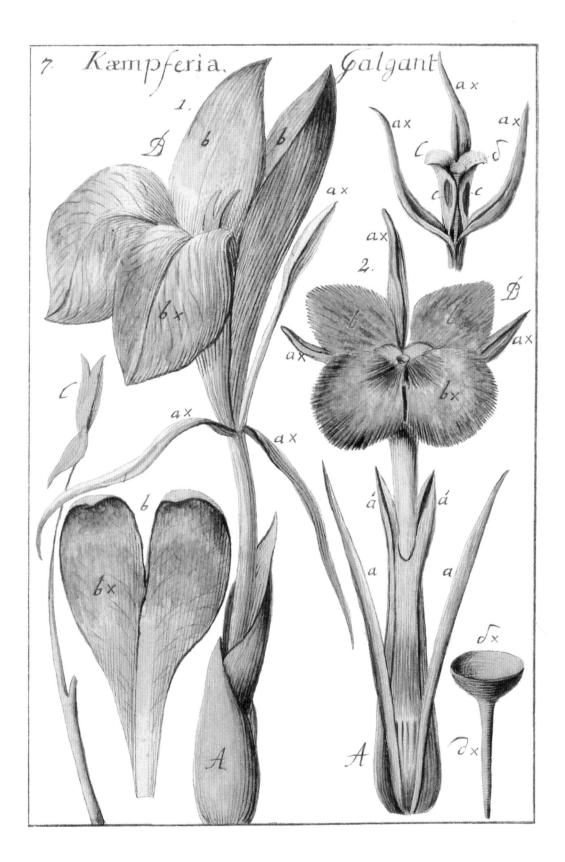

7. *Kæmpferia.* *Galgant*

30 Monday

Holiday, Republic of Ireland

31 Tuesday

Hallowe'en
RHS Flower Show

1 Wednesday

All Saint's Day
RHS Flower Show

2 Thursday

---

3 Friday

4 Saturday

First Quarter

5 Sunday

Guy Fawkes' Day

Kaempferia, a genus which Linnaeus included in Monandria, or plants with a single stamen, and which John Lindley in 1835 moved into his new family Zingiberaceae, the ginger family. Named after Engelbert Kaempfer, the first European botanist to visit Japan at the beginning of the 18th century, *Kaempferia* is grown in eastern Asia and consists of some 50 species. *Kaempferia galanga*, known as galangal, is one of the species cultivated for culinary flavourings or scent.

6   Monday

7   Tuesday

8   Wednesday

9   Thursday

10   Friday

Holiday (observed), USA

11   Saturday

Full Moon
Remembrance Day, Canada
Veterans' Day, USA

12   Sunday

Remembrance Sunday

This plate depicts Monandria, or plants with a single stamen. Jussieu made *Canna* (top row) the characteristic genus of Cannae (now Cannaceae), and *Musa,* the banana (bottom row) that of Musae (now Musaceae). In the second row, *Maranta* and *Thalia* now fall into Marantaceae, a family established by Otto Petersen in 1888, while all the rest are now in Zingiberaceae, a family established by John Lindley in 1835.

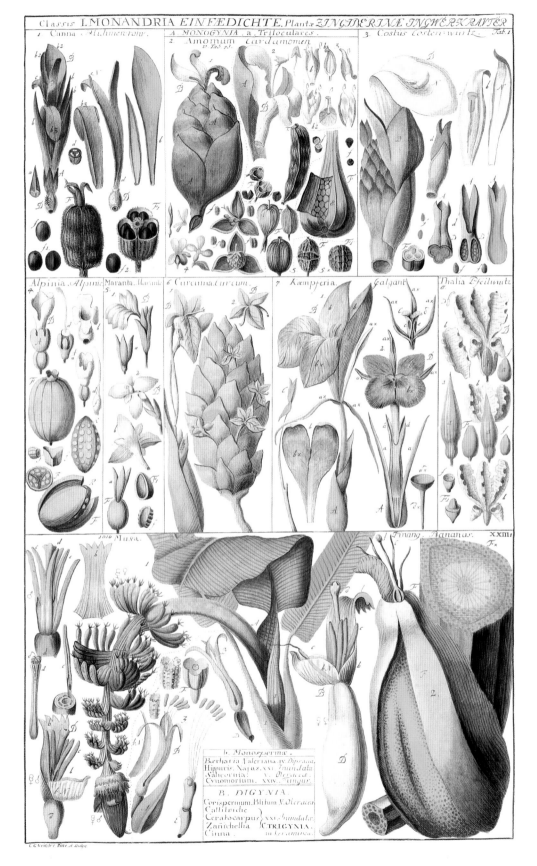

1. Canna Blumenrohr.

2. A MONOGYNIA a. Triloculares.
Amomum Cardamomen.

3. Costus Costen=wurtz. Tab. I.

4. Alpinia Alpinie.

5. Maranta Maranta.

6. Curcuma Curcum.

7. Kæmpferia Galgant.

8. Thalia Pfeilwurtz.

1016 Musa. Pisang Bananas. XXIII.

b. Monosperma.
Berhatia Valeriana. IV. Diperiata.
Hippuris. Najas. XXI. Inundata.
Salicornia. V. Oleracea.
Cynomorium. XXV. Fungus.

B. DIGYNIA.
Corispermum, Blitum. V. Oleracea.
Callitriche.
Cerabocarpus. XXI. Inundata.
Zanichellia. C. TRIGYNIA.
Cinna; in Gramina.

C. G. Geißler. Bild. d. Sculps.

Guilandina. Bonduc.
464. NierenHoltz
Adenanthera. Druesen
-Blum. Mandsiadi.
472.

13 Monday

14 Tuesday

15 Wednesday

16 Thursday

17 Friday

18 Saturday

Last Quarter

19 Sunday

Two genera which Linnaeus included in
Decandria, or plants with ten stamens, and which
Jussieu in 1789 transferred to Leguminosae, the
pea family. *Adenanthera* is a genus of tropical Asian
timber trees, the most important commercially
being *A. pavonina*, the red sandalwood. *Guilandia*
(more commonly *Guilandina*) was broken up in the
19th century, with most of its species transferred
into *Caesalpinia* and others into *Gymnocladus*.

November 2000

---

20 Monday

---

21 Tuesday

RHS Flower Show

---

22 Wednesday

RHS Flower Show

---

23 Thursday

Holiday, USA (Thanksgiving Day)

---

24 Friday

---

25 Saturday

New Moon

---

26 Sunday

Almost all the plants in this plate of Decandria, or plants with ten stamens, belong to a single natural group, established by Jussieu in 1789 as Leguminosae, the pea family (now sometimes divided into Papilionaceae, Mimosaceae and Caesalpiniaceae). Top row: *Sophora, Anagyris, Cercis, Bauhinia* and *Parkinsonia*; second row: *Cassia, Caesalpinia* (which has absorbed *Poinciana* and *Guilandia*) and *Adenanthera*; third row: *Haematoxylum, Tamarindus, Mimosa, Gleditsia*; bottom row: *Ceratonia* and *Cynometra*. The exceptions are *Anacardium* (Anacardiaceae), *Dictamnus* (Rutaceae) and *Guaiacum* (Zygophyllaceae).

Tab. 28

Classis X. DECANDRIA ZEHENFÆDICHTE. A. Monogynia. LOMENTACEÆ & varia. FARBHOLTER.

Sophora, Hosten-Bohne. Anagyris, Stink-Baum. Cercis, Judas-Baum. Bauhinia. Bauhinien. Parkinsonia, Annanas.

Cassia. Cassien. Senet-Blätter. Poinciana, Pfauen-Schwantz. Cæsalpinia, Cappan-Gelb Farb-Holtz. Guilandina, Bonduc Nieren-Holtz. Adenanthera, Drusen-Blum. Mundstad.

Hæmatoxylon, Campeche-Holtz. Tamarindus. Tamarinden. Mimosa. Acacia, Empfindlich-Kraut XXIII.1. Gleditsia, Honig-Hülse.

Ceratonia, Johanns-Brod. Guajacum, Frantzosen-Holtz. Cynometra. Hunds-Gliel. Anacardium, Acajou, Caschau. Dictamnus, Weisser-Diptam. Fraxinelle.

591. Mesua, Rosen Castanien.

November/December 2000

27 Monday

28 Tuesday

First Day of Ramadán (subject to sighting of moon)

29 Wednesday

30 Thursday

St Andrew's Day

1 Friday

2 Saturday

3 Sunday

Advent Sunday

Mesua, a genus which Linnaeus included in Polyandria, or plants with more than twenty stamens, and which Jussieu in 1789 moved into his new family Guttiferae. There are 40 species of *Mesua*, all Indian and Malaysian trees, the best-known being *Mesua ferrea*, the ironwood tree, traditionally used in India for railway sleepers.

4   Monday

First Quarter

5   Tuesday

6   Wednesday

7   Thursday

8   Friday

9   Saturday

10   Sunday

This plate depicts Polyandria, or plants with more than twenty stamens. Four of the plants in the top row were included by Jussieu in his family Capparides (now Capparidaceae): *Morisonia, Crateva, Capparis* and *Marcgravia* (later separated into Marcgraviaceae). *Breynia* is included in Euphorbiaceae, *Mammea, Calophyllum* and *Mesua* in Guttiferae, *Ochna* in Ochnaceae, *Chrysobalanus* in Chrysobalanaceae, *Microcos* in Tiliaceae, *Elaeocarpus* in Elaeaocarpaceae, *Vateria* in Dipterocarpaceae, *Mentzelia* in Loasaceae and *Plinia* in Myrtaceae.

Tab. 35.

Classis XIII. POLYANDRIA, *VIELFÆDICHTE.* A. Monogynia.

Morisonia. *Morisonien.* 2. *Stylo brevi vel nullo,* PVTAMINEÆ. SCHALICHTE. Cratæva. *Tapia Lauhapfel*

Breynia *Breynien*

Marcgrafia. *Marcgrafum.*

Capparis, *Lappern.*

Mammea, *Mameibaum.* 3. *Varia stylo elongato.* Chrysobalanus. Calophyllum. *Calaba.* Microcos. *Kleine lajas.*

Ochna. *Jabatapita.*

Elæiocarpos. *Zeilanische Olive.* Mesua. *Rosen Castanien.* Vateria. *Gumi Anime.* Mentzelia *Mentzdien.* Plinia. *Plinien.*

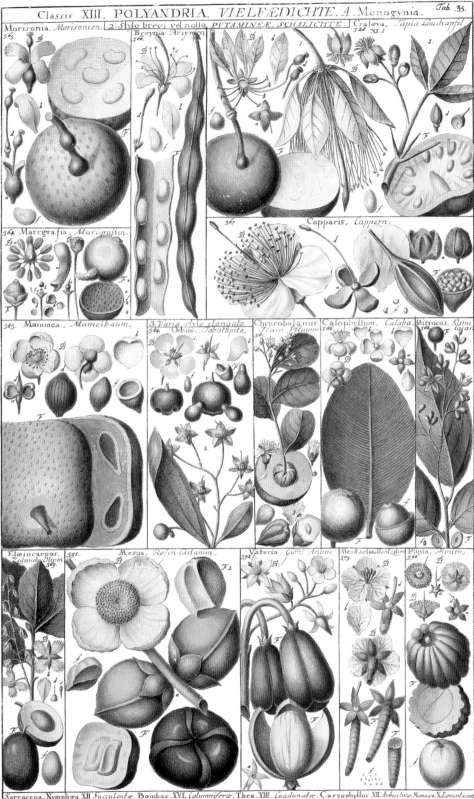

11 Monday

Full Moon

12 Tuesday

RHS Christmas Show

13 Wednesday

RHS Christmas Show

14 Thursday

15 Friday

16 Saturday

17 Sunday

Cornus, a genus which Linnaeus included in Tetrandria, or plants with four stamens. Jussieu in 1789 moved it into his family Caprifolia (Caprifoliaceae), but in 1829 the French botanist Dumortier made it the characteristic genus of a new family, Cornaceae. The common name dogwood is sometimes said to derive from the use of the wood to make dogs (grappling poles), but the word 'dogberry' was as common as 'dogwood' in early gardening literature.

18 Monday

Last Quarter

19 Tuesday

20 Wednesday

21 Thursday

Josh

Winter Solstice

22 Friday

Mum

Jewish Festival of Chanukah, First Day

23 Saturday

24 Sunday

MICKY Dosser

Christmas Eve

Of these fifteen Tetrandria, or plants with four stamens, only *Epimedium* and *Leontice* are considered today to belong to the same family (Berberidaceae). The rest are (top row): *Cornus* (Cornaceae), *Oldenlandia* (Rubiaceae), *Ammannia* (Lythraceae); middle row: *Isnardia* [now *Ludwigia*] (Onagraceae), *Trapa* (Trapaceae), *Elaeagnus* (Elaeagneaceae), *Brabejum* (Proteaceae) and *Amyris*, indicated by its specific ephithet *Elemifera* (Rutaceae); bottom row: *Hamamelis* (Hamamelidaceae), *Cuscuta* (Convulvulaceae), *Hypecoum* (Fumariaceae), *Ilex* (Aquifoliaceae) and *Coldenia* (Boraginaceae).

Tab. 10

138 Epimedium Bischoff-Hut · 139 Leontice Lowen-blatt · 140 Cornus Cornel-Kirsche · 143 Oldenlandia · 144 Amanta

A MONOGYNIA a Monopetala completa

145 Imardia · 146 Trapa Wasser-Nuss · 148 Eleagnus Oehlweide C Incompleta 147 Protium Æthiopisches Mandel-baum · 149 Salvadora v Appen Elemiera Gum Elem

b Monopetala incompleta

149 Tomex · 141 Phita · Ludwigia v Calvicanthus · 142 Dorstenia v Scabrida · 150 Rivinia 152 Camphorosma 153 Alchimilla v Gensecar

B DIGYNIA · 155 Hamamelis Virginische Pistacie · 156 Corrada Sith-Inad Hypecoum Horn-Kümme · 159 Ilex Stechpalmen · 160 Cold-no

C TETRAGYNIA

158 Potamogeton 161 Ruppia v Trund 162 Sagina v Caryophyll 157 Tillæa v

CORYDALES 138 305 139 Nolanthus T 43 Penzacula 115 Saxaria T 42 Fumaria T 46 Impatiens T 94

158. Ilex   Stechpalmen.

December 2000

---

25 Monday

New Moon
Christmas Day
Holiday, UK, Republic of Ireland,
Canada, USA, Australia and New Zealand

---

26 Tuesday

Boxing Day (St Stephen's Day)
Holiday, UK, Republic of Ireland, Canada,
Australia and New Zealand

---

27 Wednesday

---

28 Thursday

---

29 Friday

Jewish Festival of Chanukah, Eighth Day

---

30 Saturday

---

31 Sunday

Ilex, a genus which Linnaeus included in
Tetrandria, or plants with four stamens, and
which now falls into the family Aquifoliaceae.
Aquifolium, the traditional Latin name for holly,
was retained by Linnaeus for the specific epithet
in *Ilex aquifolium*. *Ilex* was the traditional name for
the holm oak; Linnaeus, grouping the oaks into
the genus *Quercus*, called the holm oak *Quercus
ilex*, but then felt entitled to re-use *Ilex* as a name
for a completely different genus.

European National Holidays 2000

Holidays that fall on a Sunday are not included

AUSTRIA	Jan. 1, 6; April 24; May 1; June 1, 12, 22; Aug. 15; Oct. 26; Nov. 1; Dec. 8, 25, 26
BELGIUM	Jan. 1; April 24; May 1; June 1, 12; July 21; Aug. 15; Nov. 1, 2, 11; Dec. 25, 26
DENMARK	Jan. 1; April 20, 21, 24; May 19; June 1, 5, 12; Dec. 25, 26
FINLAND	Jan. 1, 6; April 21, 24; May 1; June 1, 24; Nov. 4; Dec. 6, 25, 26
FRANCE	Jan. 1; April 24; May. 1, 8; June 1, 12; July 14; Aug. 15; Nov. 1, 11; Dec. 25
GERMANY	Jan. 1, 6; April 21, 24; June 1, 12; Aug. 15; Oct. 3, 31; Nov. 1; Dec. 25, 26
GREECE	Jan. 1, 6; Mar. 13, 25; April 28; May 1; June 19; Aug. 15; Oct. 28; Dec. 25, 26
ITALY	Jan. 1, 6; April 24, 25; May 1; Aug. 15; Nov. 1; Dec. 8, 25, 26
LUXEMBOURG	Jan. 1; Mar. 6; April 24; May 1; June 1, 12, 23; Aug. 15; Nov. 1, 2; Dec. 25, 26
NETHERLANDS	Jan. 1; April 21, 24; May 5; June 1, 12; Dec. 25, 26
NORWAY	Jan. 1; April 20, 21, 24; May 1, 17; June 1, 12; Dec. 25, 26
PORTUGAL	Jan. 1; Mar. 7; April 21, 24, 25; May 1; June 10, 22; Aug. 15; Oct. 5; Nov. 1; Dec. 1, 8, 25
SPAIN	Jan. 1, 6; April 20, 21; May 1; June 1; Aug. 15; Dec. 8, 25
SWEDEN	Jan. 1, 6; April 21, 24; May 1; June 1, 12, 24; Nov. 4; Dec. 25, 26
SWITZERLAND	Jan. 1; April 21, 24; May 1; June 1, 12; Aug. 1; Dec. 25, 26

Rose Cottage
Salter forth

R
Sinkey